Pavilion
PUBLISHING

CW00407697

Direct
Power

A resource pack for people
who want to develop their own
care plans and support networks

Alan Leader

Direct Power is a joint publication
by the Community Support Network,
Brixton Community Sanctuary,
Pavilion Publishing (Brighton) Ltd
and MIND.

MIND

Direct Power
Alan Leader

Direct Power is a joint publication by the Community Support Network,
Brixton Community Sanctuary and Pavilion Publishing (Brighton) Ltd and MIND.

© Pavilion Publishing 1995.

Alan Leader has asserted his rights in accordance with the Copyright, Designs and Patents Act, 1988 to be identified as the author of this work.

Pavilion Publishing (Brighton) Ltd.
8 St George's Place
Brighton, East Sussex BN1 4GB
Telephone: 01273 623222

Fax: 01273 625526

MIND
The National Association for Mental Health
Granta House, 15/19 Broadway
London E15 4BQ

Telephone: 0181 519 2122

Fax: 0181 522 1725

Information line: 0181 522 1728

Community Support Network
c/o Community Care Forum
336 Brixton Road, London SW9 7AA

Telephone: 0171 738 7826

Brixton Community Sanctuary
St Vincent's Centre
Talma Road, Brixton
London SW2 1AU

Telephone: 0171 924 0913

ISBN 1 871080 27 4

A catalogue record for this book is available from the British Library.

Editor: Anna McGrail

Design and typesetting: Stanford Douglas

Printed by: Ashford Press (Southampton)

Contents

About the Author

Alan Leader is a survivor of psychiatry and a whole range of social care institutions of different regimes.

He is currently employed as a Co-ordinator of Lambeth Community Care Forum which is a federation of voluntary sector agencies, users of Community Care Services and their carers who are all centrally involved in Community Care Services, Policy and Practice in Lambeth. Alan is a founder member of Brixton Community Sanctuary and the Community Support Network and is a member of Survivors Speak Out. He has experience at providing training seminars in Community Care issues from a user's perspective and has contributed articles on Mental Health, Community Care, and Community Development issues in a number of publications.

About the Organisations

The Community Support Network
The Community Support Network is a national umbrella organisation that aims to develop a range of user-controlled projects and alternatives to the present mental health services. The Community Support Network also aims to provide information and advice to users of mental health services who wish to develop self-advocacy initiatives.

Brixton Community Sanctuary
Brixton Community Sanctuary is a community-based resource centre that is run for and by people with experience of mental and emotional distress. The Sanctuary provides a safe, warm and supportive environment, where individuals can get advice and information and participate in a range of social, cultural, educational and empowering activities.

Acknowledgements

A lot of people have provided help and support in the development of this pack. We would like to acknowledge their efforts and support: Dave Skull, Caroline Kerslake, Hugh Lansdowne, Ken Rayburn, Peter Rothwell, Dick Leaman, Jackie Downer, Karen Davis, Janette Barr, Simon Davis, Steve Brewer, Colin Mahoney, Julie Vassili, Amita Patel, Nicola Deakin, Claire Dempster, Alan Hartman, Anne Davis, Paul Baker, Nigel Rose, Clara Buckley, Mr and Mrs Ince, Anne McDowall, Jane Lewis, Amanda Knoph, Susan Osbourne, Steve Stokes, Michael Charles, Frank Bangay, Louise Pembroke, Stephen Forbes, Lucy Taylor and many others.

' In the mental patients' liberation movement we have examined the ways in which we were treated when we 'went crazy'. Occasional instances of kindness and compassion stand out in sharp contrast to the overwhelming isolation and contempt imposed by most forms of 'treatment'. We came together to express our anger and despair at the way we were treated. Out of that process has grown the conviction that we must set up our own alternatives, because nothing that currently exists, or is proposed, fundamentally alters the unequal power relationships that are at the heart of the present mental health system.'

Judi Chamberlin: *On Our Own*.

**Dedicated to the memory of
Orville Blackwood and other victims of psychiatry.**

Introduction

Welcome to the Direct Power pack

This pack is aimed at people who have experienced mental and emotional distress, or those who have been in contact with mental health services, but want to develop their own support networks and a care plan that is tailored to their own individual needs.

Community Support Network and Brixton Community Sanctuary who produced this pack believe that:

◆ Individuals are unique.

◆ They are of unlimited worth.

◆ They have the right to the means and resources which enable them to live a full life in the community.

◆ They have the right to self-determination and to be able to develop a support network that is tailored to their individual needs.

◆ They have the right to be consulted with and to participate in the planning, management and development of local services.

Both the Community Support Network and Brixton Community Sanctuary reject the notion that people who experience or have experienced mental distress must be 'managed' and therefore need a mental health professional to guide them in the art of being a human.

Both organisations also want to break the assumption held by so many professionals that those people who refuse to take up the services they offer, or the expertise they possess, do so due to their mental distress.

In our collective experience, people refuse to take up services because in their experience they have found that services and professionals:

♦ are oppressive and controlling

♦ see them as problems to be solved, filed and dispatched rather than human beings in need of dignity, respect and consideration

♦ crush individualism

♦ emphasise the needs and political agenda of those in charge of the services and the workers

♦ deny the people the right of citizenship

♦ promote dependency and the 'sick' role

♦ are not directly accountable to users

♦ marginalise people's natural support networks and devalue people's experiences and feelings.

We hope that **Direct Power** will act as a tool which will enable you to have a central role in developing a support and care plan that will be tailored to your individual needs.

If you feel you need help and advice in using **Direct Power**, contact your local service user group in the first instance.

We hope that you find this pack useful, and if you can provide any suggestions and criticisms or if you have any ideas which you feel will improve it then just contact us.

Community Support Network,
Brixton Community Sanctuary.

The Aims of Direct Power

The aims of **Direct Power** are:

- ◆ to guide you through the maze of community care.

- ◆ to let you develop and construct a personal profile about yourself.

- ◆ for you to comment on any service you are or have been in contact with.

- ◆ to help you to undertake a self-assessment of your needs and then to identify and make contact with agencies that may be able to provide you with appropriate support, advice and information.

- ◆ to provide you with information and advice that will enable you to develop and construct your own support network and care plan.

- ◆ to help you to identify what you and any agency need to have agreements on and how to help you develop a partnership agreement.

- ◆ to help you decide on your support needs if you are either admitted to or discharged from hospital.

How to Use Direct Power

First of all, don't panic. Read through the pack carefully — take a day or so to read the different sections.

This pack belongs to you. You can decide how you use it.

For example: You could use it when you are taking part in an assessment of your needs by another agency, or you could use it as a way of finding out more about yourself and what your needs are.

Some of you will use the whole pack, others will only find certain sections of value or relevant to their experience.

Keep this pack in a safe place: Ensure that you are the one who decides who has access to the information contained inside.

Introduction

Section One   This section explains what community care is and will show you how **Direct Power** can help you get through the maze of assessment and access to services.

Section Two   This section gives you an opportunity to write down in your own words about yourself, your present circumstances, for you to explore issues that affect you, and for you to suggest practical steps that you need to take.

Section Three   This is a space for you to write down in your own words what your experiences and feelings are about the services you have used in the past and those that you are currently in contact with. Have they helped you? If so how? If they have not helped, you can describe in your own words why you think that is.

Section Four   The aim of this section is to help you identify what your needs are.

Section Five   After you have carried out a self-assessment of your needs, this section provides a space where you can put them in order of priority.

Section Six   We hope that this section will help you to identify those agencies which can provide advice and information relating to areas that you have identified as priority needs. It also contains an ***Agency Contact Sheet*** so that you can keep a record of the contacts that you have with the agencies you have chosen to approach.

Section Seven   Once you have made contact with those agencies that are prepared to offer you a service or support, we would encourage you to enter into a partnership agreement with them. This will ensure that you are aware of:

◆ what they are offering you

◆ what they expect from you, and

◆ what you can expect from them.

Section Eight   This section is to help you think through what support you may need if you are admitted to hospital. It also includes an ***Aftercare Checklist*** which you should try to get completed before you are discharged.

Section One

Direct Power and Community Care

Direct Power has been developed over the same period that community care has come into force, at local, regional and national level. In this section we shall try to explain what community care is.

What is Community Care?

In April 1993, a new system of support was set up for disabled, frail and vulnerable people and the family and friends who look after them (carers). This system is called **Community Care** or Care Management.

What sort of support could you be entitled to?

Some examples of support are:

◆ home care or a home help

◆ meals on wheels

◆ a break from caring (sometimes called respite care)

◆ aids and equipment

◆ occupational therapy

◆ temporary or permanent accommodation in a nursing or residential home

◆ day-care services

◆ access to vocational or sheltered employment

◆ help with installing a telephone, and special equipment to help you use it

- evening classes and special interest groups
- any other support that is seen by you and Social Services as being needed, available and economic.

How can you get the help you need?

The way to get help is to request an assessment from Social Services. This assessment should take the form of a number of interviews and discussions.

In **Section Two** you will see the heading: **Current Circumstances**; listed under this heading are the types of questions that you will be asked by the person undertaking the assessment.

It's a good idea to prepare yourself for the assessment. You could do so by completing the *Current Circumstances: Checklist* (see page 21), then the *Self-assessment of Needs: Checklist* (see page 37).

You can then decide which areas are the most important in order of priority — see **Section Five** for help with this.

You will then be able to ensure that Social Services are aware of what you feel your circumstances and needs are.

An assessment should focus on your needs. However, the person doing the assessment will also take into account the needs of your family and friends (carers), and any support that they need in order to support you.

Always remind the person doing the assessment that your needs are not necessarily the same as the needs of your carers.

It is a good idea to discuss your needs with your carers and decide, where possible, what support and help you both need.

If you do not have a carer, spend some time completing the *Current Circumstances: Checklist* on page 21, and the *Self-assessment of Needs: Checklist* on page 37. Consider whether you would like an independent person (an advocate) to support you during the assessment discussions and interviews.

When you contact Social Services, ask them where you can get access to independent advocacy support. You could also ask groups such as MIND, or the Citizens' Advice Bureau for information on advocacy.

How do you get this help?

If you are already in touch with Social Services, make an appointment directly with them to discuss your request for an assessment. You will find their number in the phone book, listed under the name of your local council.

Check with them to see if you meet their criteria.

You could also ask your home help, community psychiatric nurse, local user group, or someone you are already in touch with, to contact Social Services for you.

Who can apply for help?

The Social Services must by law, assess anyone in England, Wales or Scotland who appears to need services under the **NHS and Community Care Act**.

However, each different area has a different way of deciding who can get an assessment; these decisions vary from area to area.

The Social Services department must inform you:

◆ what services it provides

◆ who is eligible to get them

◆ how they deal with applications.

This information should be available on cassette tape and in other languages.

Direct Power may help you to develop your own care plan without even using Social Services, but you should be aware of the energy and effort this will need from you.

After the assessment

After or at the assessment meetings or interview, Social Services will draw up a report of the assessment. This report is called a **care plan**.

The care plan states:

♦ what your needs are

♦ what Social Services sees your needs as being, and

♦ what Social Services propose to do to help.

Ask for a copy of your assessment form and your care plan. You should ask for it to be made available in the format that is most accessible for you.

Don't sign the care plan unless you agree that it is accurate and you are happy with it, or if you are prepared to give it a try. Discuss with Social Services the idea of having **partnership agreements**, like those in **Section Seven** with each of the agencies providing a service to meet your needs.

A care plan should identify those agencies who will provide you with a service to support you and state how your situation is going to be reviewed.

Make sure that you know what to do if you are unhappy with the services being provided. The plan should also give the name of a contact person, someone called a **Care Manager**.

What can you do if you are not happy with the way Social Services have dealt with your situation?

If you are unhappy with any aspect of the assessment carried out by Social Services, or their decision on the types and level of services they will offer you, then you have the right to challenge that decision.

Social Services must act reasonably and fairly and give reasons for their decisions.

Some of the problems that you may face are:

♦ Your request for an assessment has been refused, or there are long delays between requesting an assessment and getting one, or between getting an assessment and being offered support services.

♦ Social Services decide not to provide you with or help you gain access to community care services, even though they have assessed you as needing them.

Remember that:

◆ Doing a **self-assessment** may help you get the best out of any assessment carried out by Social Services.

◆ You may not be able to get all the services and support you need.

◆ You also have the right to refuse services.

How can you complain?

If you are not happy with your assessment, the care plan suggested or the quality of the services being offered, you can challenge these decisions.

If you want to complain, seek advice and discuss your complaint with your local Citizens' Advice Bureau, local Law Centre or Advocacy Project. This will help you to find out what are the different options — and what would be the best way for you.

Options include:

◆ Social Services complaints procedure

◆ Monitoring Officer

◆ complaint to the ombudsman

◆ action for damages

◆ judicial review

◆ default power of the Secretary of State.

You should seek legal advice on what action to take. It is a good idea to keep copies of all correspondence, and use **Direct Power**.

NB: It is also possible to receive services under the Care Programme Approach. This approach is co-ordinated within the NHS Health Trust. It is broadly the same as Community Care/Care Management, which is co-ordinated within Social Services. The Department of Health has set up these two systems, and it can be a bit confusing for all involved.

We think it is better to go through Care Management and Social Services as this system has financial resources attached to it which mean that any care plan that is negotiated should have money to back it up and make sure it happens.

In some areas Social Services and Health Services have worked out a system to combine Care Management and the Care Programme Approach, which is a step in the right direction.

Section Two

Building Your Own Personal Profile

This section has two parts

◆ Your Personal Profile

◆ Current Circumstances: Checklist.

YOUR PERSONAL PROFILE

1 **What words would you use to describe the unique person that you are?**
Please write them in the space below:

2 **What would you describe as your strengths? What do you do well?**
Please use the space below to list these things.

3 **What things would you like to learn? Are there things you would like to improve?**
Please use the space below to list these things.

4 **What are the things you enjoy?**
Please use the space below to list them:

5 **What skills and attributes do you want to see in those trying to support you?**

14

6 **When would you like to see support and help provided?**

For example: evenings, weekends, public holidays?

Can you please give reasons why you would like services to be provided at these times?

7 **What things would you like to be able to achieve, but there are blocks and obstacles stopping you from achieving them?**

What are these obstacles? For example: money, transport, housing?

What you want to achieve	What is blocking you

8 **Are you happy with the services that are being provided to you?**

*If **yes**, please give details:*

If you are unhappy, then write down your reasons.

Don't forget to identify the **agency** you are writing about.

Happy

Unhappy

9 **If you have wanted to make a complaint about a service or the agency, but did not go ahead with it, can you give your reasons why?**

10 **Have you ever made a complaint about any of the services you use?**

What was the complaint? What happened? Were you satisfied with the outcome?

State when the complaint was made — who you complained to — and what action resulted.

```




```

11 **What things need action to improve your use of the services you are in contact with?**

For example: more opportunities to talk one-to-one with workers about your needs; the provision of crèche facilities; weekend access to services.

```




```

🖸 Personal landmarks

All of us can recall various events that have affected our lives up to now. These landmarks are important as they help us review the past and to make plans for the future.

In the space below, write or draw the major events in your life.

Next to each landmark put the year and your age at the time, as a guide.

13 Important people in your life

Who are the important people in your life? Below you will find a list of categories regarding these people. Place each important person into one of these categories, and give a short statement about your relationship with that person.

Regular contact

Hardly any contact

Infrequent but regular contact

CURRENT CIRCUMSTANCES: CHECKLIST

If you are lucky enough to get an assessment under the **NHS and Community Care Act**, Social Services will want to know quite a lot about your current circumstances.

This part of the pack will help you bring all the information you will need about your current circumstances together in one place.

Once you have completed this part of the pack, keep it in a safe place and present it to those undertaking the assessments.

Your name . . . .

Address . . . .

. . . .

. . . .

. . . .

Telephone number . . . .

Date of birth . . . .

1 **Accommodation**
Please tick one of the following boxes.

Council tenant	☐	Housing association tenant	☐
Owner occupier	☐	Privately rented	☐
Nursing home	☐	Hostel	☐
Residential care home	☐	Homeless	☐
Temporary accommodation *(staying with friends/family)*	☐		

Continued on the next page…

Accommodation/continued...

Please tick one of the following boxes.

Type of accommodation

Flat ☐   House ☐

Is it supported housing? ☐   Is it shared or self-contained? ☐

Rooms

Number of rooms in your accommodation . . . .

Number of rooms you use . . . .

Do you have a: Bathroom?   Yes ☐   No ☐

Kitchen?   Yes ☐   No ☐

Toilet?   Yes ☐   No ☐

Heating?   Yes ☐   No ☐

Hot water?   Yes ☐   No ☐

---

2 **Finance**

What are your sources of income, if any? *For example: salary, pensions, welfare benefits (please state which ones you receive).*

State the amount you receive each week/month: £ . . . .

Would you like to see your benefits reviewed/increased?   Yes ☐   No ☐

Do you have any savings?   Yes ☐   No ☐

If **yes**, *how much have you got saved?*   £ . . . .

---

3 Mobility

Can you get around indoors:

With help and/or equipment?	Yes ☐	No ☐
Without help and/or equipment?	Yes ☐	No ☐

Can you climb stairs/steps inside?   Yes ☐   No ☐

Can you climb stairs/steps outside?   Yes ☐   No ☐

Are you able to use public transport?   Yes ☐   No ☐

Do you have a bus pass?   Yes ☐   No ☐

Do you have a taxi card?   Yes ☐   No ☐

Do you use Dial-a-Ride?   Yes ☐   No ☐

Do you have your own private transport?   Yes ☐   No ☐

4 Dietary Needs

Do you have a medically advised diet?   Yes ☐   No ☐

If **yes**, please give brief details . . . .

. . . .

. . . .

Are you a vegetarian?   Yes ☐   No ☐

Are you a vegan?   Yes ☐   No ☐

**Do you have a special diet due
to cultural/religious needs?**   Yes ☐   No ☐

If **yes**, please give details . . . .

. . . .

. . . .

Continued on the next page...

Dietary Needs/continued...

Do you have any food allergies?   Yes ☐   No ☐

If **yes**, please give brief details . . . .

. . . .

. . . .

**Can you afford or get access to your
required or chosen diet?**   Yes ☐   No ☐

If **no**, please state the reasons why . . . .

. . . .

. . . .

5 Activities of Daily Living

Can you carry out the following activities alone or do you need some help?

	Alone	With help
Shopping	☐	☐
Housework	☐	☐
Laundry	☐	☐
Preparing and cooking meals/drinks	☐	☐
Washing up	☐	☐
Going out alone	☐	☐
Managing money	☐	☐
Managing children	☐	☐

6 **Social Contact**

Do you live as a member of a family?	Yes ☐	No ☐	
Are you in touch with family members?	Yes ☐	No ☐	
Are family members living close enough to provide support?	Yes ☐	No ☐	

Do you live alone or with others?

Alone ☐

With others ☐

Who are they? . . . .

. . . .

. . . .

Visits
Do you have visits from any of the following and how often?

			How often?
Relatives	Yes ☐	No ☐	. . . .
Neighbours	Yes ☐	No ☐	. . . .
Friends	Yes ☐	No ☐	. . . .
Social worker	Yes ☐	No ☐	. . . .
Home help	Yes ☐	No ☐	. . . .
Community psychiatric nurse	Yes ☐	No ☐	. . . .
Doctor	Yes ☐	No ☐	. . . .
Psychiatrist	Yes ☐	No ☐	. . . .
Religious leader	Yes ☐	No ☐	. . . .
Housing officer	Yes ☐	No ☐	. . . .
Worker from voluntary organisation	Yes ☐	No ☐	. . . .
Someone else	Yes ☐	No ☐	. . . .

7 Occupation

What do you do during the day, including at weekends/bank holidays?

....

....

....

....

....

Are you employed? Yes ☐ No ☐

*If **yes**, tick one of the following boxes:*

Open employment ☐

Sheltered employment ☐

Supported employment ☐

Voluntary work ☐

Is this: Full-time ☐ Part time ☐

Are you happy with your employment situation? Yes ☐ No ☐

Would you like a change? Yes ☐ No ☐

Are you prevented from working despite wishing to do so? Yes ☐ No ☐

*If **yes**, give the reasons why:*

....

....

....

....

....

....

8 Day-care/Day Support

Do you use any of the following:

Drop-in Centre?   Yes ☐ No ☐
*If **yes**, how often do you use it?*

. . . .

Local Authority (council) or Health Service Day Centre?   Yes ☐ No ☐
*If **yes**, how often do you use it?*

. . . .

Voluntary organisation Day Centre?   Yes ☐ No ☐
*If **yes**, how often do you use it?*

. . . .

9 Education/Vocational Training

Do you attend adult education classes?   Yes ☐ No ☐
*If **yes**, what course are you on?*

. . . .

. . . .

Would you like to attend adult education classes?   Yes ☐ No ☐
*If **yes**, what subjects/courses are you interested in?*

. . . .

. . . .

Do you use any skill/vocational training schemes?   Yes ☐ No ☐
*If **yes**, what are you being trained for?*

. . . .

. . . .

10 Leisure and Recreation

Please describe any leisure or social activities that you participate in:

. . . .

. . . .

. . . .

. . . .

. . . .

Are you happy with your leisure-time situation?   Yes ☐   No ☐

What do you like doing most?

. . . .

. . . .

. . . .

Are you in any of the following:
*If **yes**, please tick one or more of the boxes below*

Clubs	☐	Religious activities	☐	Sporting activities	☐
Voluntary work	☐	Watching TV	☐	Reading	☐
Listening to music	☐	Library	☐	Having friends around	☐

Do you smoke?   Yes ☐   No ☐

Do you drink alcohol?   Yes ☐   No ☐

Do you have any pets?
*If **yes**, give details*

. . . .

. . . .

. . . .

Section Three

Experiences of Services You Are In Contact With

In this section you can take stock of the services you are in contact with, or have been in contact with. This should be helpful to you in deciding which sort of services you might currently need.

1 **Services You Are Already in Contact With/ Have Been In Contact With in the Past**

What Mental Health Services/Social Services are you in contact with at the present time? Name the agency and the worker. Please describe what service they provide for you.

Service name . . . .

Address . . . .

. . . .

Contact worker . . . .

Service provided for you . . . .

. . . .

. . . .

. . . .

. . . .

. . . .

Continued on the next page...

Services You Are Already in Contact With/continued...

Service name . . . .

Address . . . .

. . . .

Contact worker . . . .

Service provided for you . . . .

. . . .

. . . .

Service name . . . .

Address . . . .

. . . .

Contact worker . . . .

Service provided for you . . . .

. . . .

. . . .

Service name . . . .

Address . . . .

. . . .

Contact worker . . . .

Service provided for you . . . .

. . . .

. . . .

Services You Are Already in Contact With/continued...

Service name . . . .

Address . . . .

. . . .

Contact worker . . . .

Service provided for you . . . .

. . . .

. . . .

Service name . . . .

Address . . . .

. . . .

Contact worker . . . .

Service provided for you . . . .

. . . .

. . . .

Service name . . . .

Address . . . .

. . . .

Contact worker . . . .

Service provided for you . . . .

. . . .

. . . .

2 **Reasons for Contact**

Why are you in contact with the agencies, services or professionals you have named on the previous pages? How long have you been in contact with them? What have you achieved with their support?

Service or professional's name. . . . .

Your comments. . . . .

. . . .

. . . .

. . . .

. . . .

Service or professional's name. . . . .

Your comments. . . . .

. . . .

. . . .

. . . .

. . . .

Service or professional's name. . . . .

Your comments. . . . .

. . . .

. . . .

. . . .

. . . .

Reasons for Contact/continued...

Service or professional's name. . . . .

Your comments. . . . .

. . . .

. . . .

. . . .

. . . .

. . . .

Service or professional's name. . . . .

Your comments. . . . .

. . . .

. . . .

. . . .

. . . .

. . . .

Service or professional's name. . . . .

Your comments. . . . .

. . . .

. . . .

. . . .

. . . .

. . . .

3 **How Services See You**

What words or phrases do mental health workers/social work professionals use to describe you and your experiences? Wherever possible, put down their name and their job title; for example: psychiatrist, social worker, nurse.

Write down any words they use to describe you and your experiences. Also write down what you think of the words, descriptions and labels they use.

Professional's name/title	Words they used	Your views

How Services See You/continued...

Professional's name/title	Words they used	Your views

How Services See You/continued...

Now that you have reviewed the services you have either used or are using, describe here: the **ideal** service to meet your needs, and the service you definitely **don't** want.

Ideal service for me	Service I do not want

Section Four

Self-assessment of Needs: Checklist

Getting help, advice and support for any area of our lives, or for the problems we have, is often very time-consuming, stressful and anxiety-provoking. Even when we have been able to make contact with organisations, or the various departments of the Council or the Health Authorities, they very often want to carry out their own assessment of your needs before they consider offering you any support or a particular service.

Sometimes, they don't seem to understand what you think is a priority.

One of the aims of **Direct Power** is to help you compile a profile of yourself and the services you are already in contact with. This section aims to help you identify those areas where you feel you need support and advice. (You can move on to putting these areas in some kind of priority order in **Section Five**)

We hope that once you have completed this section, it will enable you to make sure your concerns are known to agencies and professionals.

How to complete your self-assessment

These self-assessment sections have been designed so that they are easy to complete.

1. First of all, study the boxes on the next pages very carefully. Place a tick in those boxes where you feel you need or would benefit from help and support.

2. Once you have done this, turn to **Section Five**, *Priority Action List*. There, in order of priority, put down the box number in the space provided. Then, in your own words, write down why you need help and advice in that area.

3. When you have completed **Section Five**, you can either check the services you are presently in contact with to see if they can help you, or move on to **Section Six** and see if the **Help and Support Directory** can put you in contact with an agency who may be able to help.

Also in **Section Six** you will find an *Agency Contact Sheet*, (we suggest that you photocopy this sheet a few times). These sheets can help you keep a record of your contact with these agencies.

1 Dealing with anxiety and panic attacks	☐	**2** Dealing with agoraphobia	☐
3 Coping with depression	☐	**4** Anger and frustration	☐
5 Bereavement	☐	**6** Sexual problems	☐
7 Hearing voices	☐	**8** Loneliness and isolation	☐
9 Information on talking treatments	☐	**10** Family therapy	☐
11 Counselling (women)	☐	**12** Counselling (men)	☐

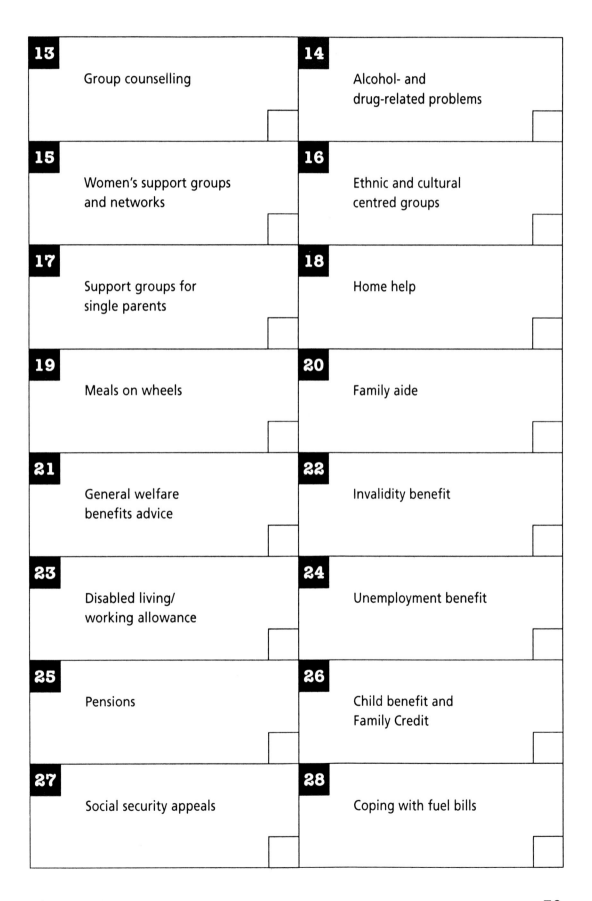

13	Group counselling	14	Alcohol- and drug-related problems
15	Women's support groups and networks	16	Ethnic and cultural centred groups
17	Support groups for single parents	18	Home help
19	Meals on wheels	20	Family aide
21	General welfare benefits advice	22	Invalidity benefit
23	Disabled living/ working allowance	24	Unemployment benefit
25	Pensions	26	Child benefit and Family Credit
27	Social security appeals	28	Coping with fuel bills

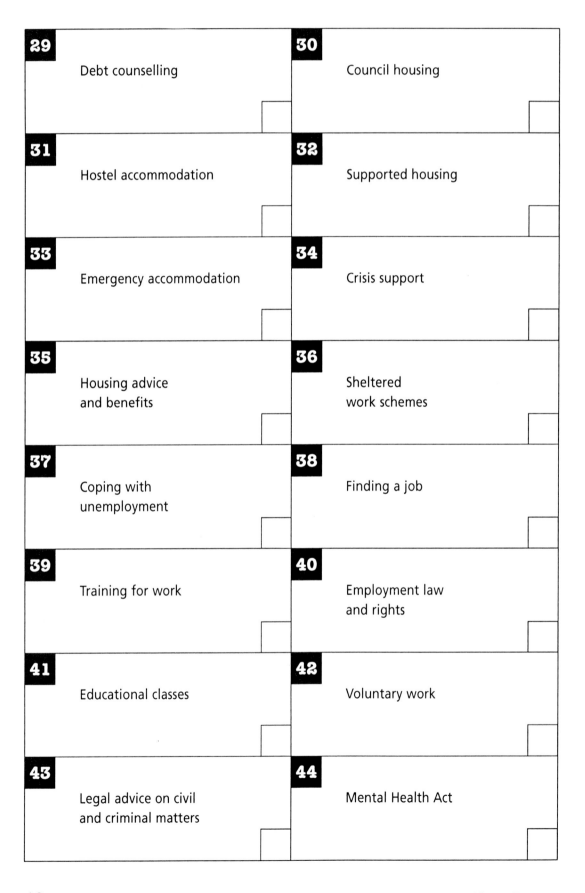

29 Debt counselling ☐	**30** Council housing ☐
31 Hostel accommodation ☐	**32** Supported housing ☐
33 Emergency accommodation ☐	**34** Crisis support ☐
35 Housing advice and benefits ☐	**36** Sheltered work schemes ☐
37 Coping with unemployment ☐	**38** Finding a job ☐
39 Training for work ☐	**40** Employment law and rights ☐
41 Educational classes ☐	**42** Voluntary work ☐
43 Legal advice on civil and criminal matters ☐	**44** Mental Health Act ☐

45 Information on medication or treatment	**46** Information about citizens' advocacy
47 Information on advocacy	**48** Befriending schemes
49 Support groups (general)	**50** Support groups (specific)
51 Services for elderly people	**52** Services for young people
53 Travel passes	**54** Telephone
55 Disability aids in the home	**56** Day centres
57 Drop-in and social clubs	**58** Day-hospital services
59 Obtaining a social worker	**60** Contacting a community psychiatric nurse

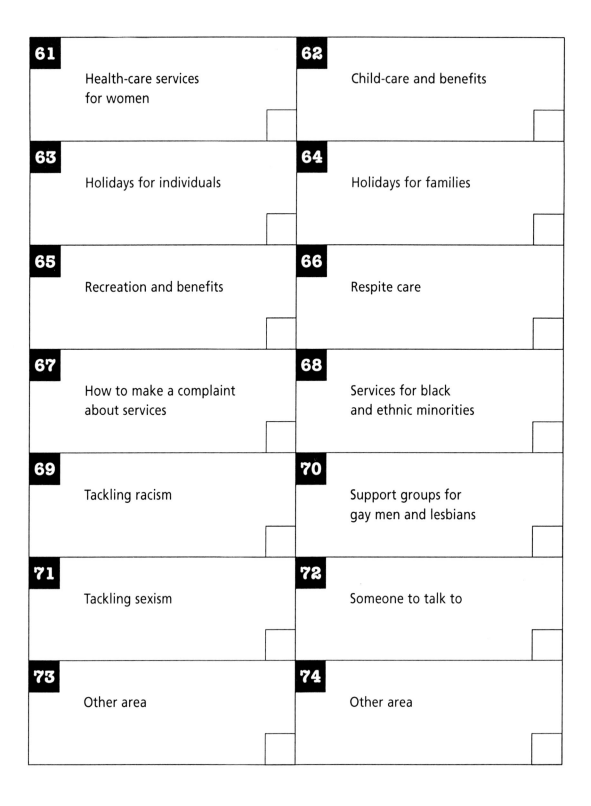

61 Health-care services for women	**62** Child-care and benefits
63 Holidays for individuals	**64** Holidays for families
65 Recreation and benefits	**66** Respite care
67 How to make a complaint about services	**68** Services for black and ethnic minorities
69 Tackling racism	**70** Support groups for gay men and lesbians
71 Tackling sexism	**72** Someone to talk to
73 Other area	**74** Other area

Section Five

Priority Action List

Now, using the information from **Section Four**, make a list of your top ten priorities. Put the box number and the area you need support with, and then in your own words, state what help you are looking for.

Priority 1

Box Number ☐ Area of support ☐

. . . .

. . . .

. . . .

Priority 2

Box Number ☐ Area of support ☐

. . . .

. . . .

. . . .

. . . .

Priority 3

Box Number [ ] Area of support [ ]

. . . .

. . . .

. . . .

. . . .

Priority 4

Box Number [ ] Area of support [ ]

. . . .

. . . .

. . . .

. . . .

Priority 5

Box Number [ ] Area of support [ ]

. . . .

. . . .

. . . .

. . . .

Priority **6**

Box Number ☐ Area of support ☐

. . . .

. . . .

. . . .

. . . .

Priority **7**

Box Number ☐ Area of support ☐

. . . .

. . . .

. . . .

. . . .

Priority **8**

Box Number ☐ Area of support ☐

. . . .

. . . .

. . . .

. . . .

Section Five: Priority Action List

Priority █9█

Box Number ☐   Area of support ☐

. . . .

. . . .

. . . .

. . . .

Priority █10█

Box Number ☐   Area of support ☐

. . . .

. . . .

. . . .

. . . .

Section Six

Further Help and Support/ Agency Contact Sheet

This section has two parts:

◆   Further Help and Support

◆   Agency Contact Sheet.

Further Help and Support

This section should be used once you have completed the **Self-assessment of Needs: Checklist**; it aims to provide you with a basic list of agencies that may be able to provide you with advice and support.

The list in this book is a list of national organisations, who may have branches or offices in your local area. The Head Office will be able to put you in touch with your local branch.

Following the name of each agency, you will find some numbers; these numbers refer to the corresponding boxes in the **Self-assessment of Needs: Checklist.** This makes it easy to see which agencies might be able to help you with the needs you have identified.

Wherever you live, there may be a directory of mental health services for you to use. Ask for this at Social Services, Health Services, your local Citizens' Advice Bureau or your local MIND association.

We have also included a page in this book headed **Local Contacts**. This will help you to keep a record of useful names, addresses and contact names and numbers of organisations and agencies who can offer support and advice in your local area.

To keep a record of your contact with any of these agencies or organisations, we suggest that you photocopy the *Agency Contact Sheet* on **page 55**. Use a copy of this sheet to keep notes about each agency you make contact with.

Good luck.

Further Help and Support

Agency	Self-assessment of Needs: Checklist Box Number

MIND . . . . | 1 | 2 | 3 | 4 | 44 | 45 |
The National Association for Mental Health
Granta House, 15/19 Broadway
London E15 4BQ
Telephone: 0181 522 1725

Alcohol Concern . . . . | 11 | 12 | 14 |
305 Grays Inn Road
London WC1X 8QF
Telephone: 0171 833 3471/ 0171 278 2126

Alcohol Counselling Service . . . . | 11 | 12 | 13 | 14 |
34 Electric Lane
London SW9 8JT
Telephone: 0171 737 3579

British Association for Counselling . . . . | 9 | 10 | 11 | 12 | 13 |
1 Regent Place
Rugby CV21 2PJ
Telephone: 01788 578328

Community Service Volunteers . . . . | 37 | 42 |
237 Pentonville Road
London N1 9NG
Telephone: 0171 278 6601

Community Support Network . . . . | 8 | 17 | 22 | 24 | 25 | 27 | 28 | 33 | 42 | 44 |
c/o Lambeth Community Care Forum | 45 | 46 | 47 | 57 | 67 | 70 | 45 | 45 | 45 | 45 |
336 Brixton Road
London SW9 7AA
Telephone: 0171 274 2299

Cruse . . . . | 5 |
(The National Organisation for the
Widowed and their Children)
126 Sheen Road
Richmond, Surrey TW9 1UK
Telephone: 0181 940 4818

Family Welfare Association.................. 10 11 12 13
Central Office
501–505 Kingsland Road
London E8 4AU
Telephone: 0171 254 6251

Gingerbread............................. 26 52 62
(Association for One-parent Families)
35 Wellington Street
London WC2E 7BN
Telephone: 0171 240 0953

Holiday Care Services...................... 63 64
2 Old Bank Chambers
Station Road
Horley
Surrey
Telephone: 01923-774535

Housing Campaign for Single People 30 31 32 33 34 35
5–15 Cramer Street
London WC1H 8LS
Telephone: 0171 833 2071

Housing Debtline 29 70
Telephone: 0121 359 8501/2/3
(Telephone advice service for people
in trouble with rent, mortgage arrears
and other debt problems.)

National Association for 31 32
Voluntary Hostels
Fulham Palace
Bishops Avenue
London SW6
Telephone: 0171 731-4205

National Childcare Campaign................. 17 26 42
Kingsway House
4 Wild Court
London WC2B 6ST
Telephone: 0171 405 5617

Direct Power

National Citizens' Advocacy 46
Unit 2k, Leroy House
436 Essex Road
London N1 3QP
Telephone: 0171 359 8289

Pre-school Playgroups Association. 17 52 62
61–63 Kings Cross Road
London WC1X 9LL
Telephone: 0171 833-0991

Survivors Speak Out. 1 9 45
34 Osnaburgh Street
London NW1 3ND
Telephone: 0171 916 6991

United Kingdom Advocacy Network (UKAN) 45 46 47
Premier House
14 Cross Burgess Street
Sheffield S1 2HG
Telephone: 0114 275 3131

Women's Therapy Centre. 9 11 13 49 50 61
6 Manor Gardens
London N7 6LA
Telephone: 0171 263 6200

Worklink (Assessment) 36 37 38 39 41
336 Brixton Road
London SW9 7AA
Telephone: 0171 274 2299

LOCAL CONTACTS

Name . . . .

Address . . . .

. . . .

. . . .

Telephone No. . . . .

Name . . . .

Address . . . .

. . . .

. . . .

Telephone No. . . . .

Name . . . .

Address . . . .

. . . .

. . . .

Telephone No. . . . .

Name . . . .

Address . . . .

. . . .

. . . .

Telephone No. . . . .

Name   . . . .

Address   . . . .

              . . . .

              . . . .

Telephone No. . . . .

Name   . . . .

Address   . . . .

              . . . .

              . . . .

Telephone No. . . . .

Name   . . . .

Address   . . . .

              . . . .

              . . . .

Telephone No. . . . .

Name   . . . .

Address   . . . .

              . . . .

              . . . .

Telephone No. . . . .

Agency Contact Sheet

The aim of the *Agency Contact Sheet* is to help you to keep a record of all your contact with the agencies from whom you seek advice, help and support. This sheet will help you record what took place and allow you to note down what further action needs to be taken.

Photocopy the page before you start filling it in. This will mean that you have spare copies; also it may be a good idea to have **one sheet for each agency you contact**.

Write things down clearly so it is easy to see what stage things are at with each agency.

We have some tips that may prove to be useful, that we would like to pass on to you.

◆ Before you make contact with an agency or organisation, jot down on your **Contact Sheet** under **Purpose of Contact** the main points you want to make or raise.

◆ Once these points have been asked and answers have been given to your satisfaction, tick them off.

◆ Make a note on your **Contact Sheet** of what the agency tells you; don't be frightened to ask workers to repeat items or to clarify points you are not sure of.

◆ After making contact, review the situation and decide what your next step should be.

Good luck.

AGENCY CONTACT SHEET

Name of agency . . . .

Address . . . .

. . . .

Telephone number . . . .

Contact person . . . .

Directions to agency *Bus routes, landmarks and so on* . . . .

. . . .

Date of contact	Purpose of contact	Person spoken to	Follow-up action

Agency Contact Sheet/continued

Date of contact	Purpose of contact	Person spoken to	Follow-up action

Section Seven

Partnership Agreements

If you find an organisation that is prepared to offer you a service or give support, we would advise you to ask them to enter into a partnership agreement with you.

A partnership agreement will be a way of ensuring that you are clear about:

◆ what is being offered

◆ for what purpose

◆ what responsibilities the organisation has to you, and

◆ what your responsibilities are.

A partnership agreement would include the following details:

◆ the name of the organisation and its address and telephone number

◆ the name of the person you should liaise with

◆ the purpose of you receiving support/help/advice from this organisation

◆ when, where and how this support will be given

◆ what exactly the organisation is going to provide

◆ when progress will be reviewed

◆ what can you do if you are unhappy about the service provided.

Please ensure that YOU and the AGENCY both keep a signed copy of the partnership agreement.

PARTNERSHIP AGREEMENT

This is a partnership agreement between you and the agency that provides you with a service.

Your name

Name of agency

Address

Address

Telephone number

Telephone number

Please give the name of your contact at the agency and what position they hold.

What services do you want the agency to provide?

What are the services that the agency has agreed to offer you? *Write down where, when and how.*

What do you and the agency hope to achieve by working together?

When will progress be reviewed and who will be involved?

Review Date	Name of worker	Telephone no.

Whom should you contact if you are unhappy about the services offered or wish to make a complaint?

Any other information you may wish to record.

Your signature   **Signature of agency worker**

Date . . . .   Date . . . .

Section Eight

Hospital and Home

Section Eight has three parts:

◆ Hospital Admission

◆ Money and Bills

◆ Discharge and Aftercare

Hospital Admission

This section contains a **Hospital Information Sheet** which you may find useful if:

◆ you are going to be admitted to hospital, *or*

◆ you have been admitted to hospital, *or*

◆ you have had admissions in the past and feel you may again in the future.

The aim of completing the **Hospital Information Sheet** (see page 63) will be to try to avoid adding further distress to an already distressing situation. Completing this Sheet will help to make sure your views are listened to, at a time when communicating your views may be very difficult.

When the **Hospital Information Sheet** is complete, keep a copy. Also, decide who you trust most to carry out some of the tasks you have identified as being important to you. This could be a friend, a family member, a professional, a service user group or any other agency that you identify and have an agreement with.

The identified person/persons can have a copy of the **Hospital Information Sheet**, or you might decide to give selected information to different people if that is what would work best for you. This information can be updated or changed when necessary.

NB: *The Mental Health Act* (1983) has various sections which cover compulsory detention in hospital and others that cover after-care. If the Mental Health Act applies to you, you may need the help of an advocate so that you are fully informed of your rights both in hospital and living in the community.

HOSPITAL INFORMATION SHEET

If I am admitted to hospital, I want the following to be taken into consideration:-

1 **I would like the following people to be told that I have been admitted to hospital:**

◆ immediately *(for example: Partner/trusted friend/next of kin, children)*:

. . . .

. . . .

◆ other people to tell *(for example: milkman/home-help/work/college/ window cleaner)*:

. . . .

. . . .

. . . .

2 **I would like the following people not to be told that I'm in hospital:**

. . . .

. . . .

. . . .

3 **I would particularly like the following person/people to visit me:**

. . . .

. . . .

4 **I would not like the following person/people to visit me without my prior consent:**

. . . .

. . . .

5 **I want to be consulted before any information regarding my health or treatment is given to others.** Yes ☐ No ☐

Continued on the next page...

Children

If you have young children at home and would like them to be cared for while you are in hospital, please fill out this section.

6 **I would like the following people to look after my children while I am in hospital:**

. . . .

. . . .

What I would like to see happen, if possible, is:

. . . .

. . . .

7 **If I am unable to, I would like the following people to explain to my child/children why I am in hospital:**

. . . .

. . . .

I would like them to be told:

. . . .

. . . .

Pets

If you have pets and would like them to be cared for while you are in hospital, please fill out this section.

8 **I have the following pets:**

. . . .

I would like the following people to look after my pets:

. . . .

. . . .

9 **Some information about caring for my pets that people need know is:**

. . . .

. . . .

If you have been in hospital before

10   **In the past, these things have worked well or helped me make a recovery:**

. . . .

. . . .

11   **In the past, these things did not work well or made life more difficult during my time in hospital:**

. . . .

. . . .

12   **What I would like to see happen this time is:**

. . . .

. . . .

13   **Things that have changed since my last admission, and which I think are relevant to how I want to be treated this time are:**

. . . .

. . . .

Food and drink

Do you follow a special diet or have particular dislikes for certain foods or allergies to food that you would like hospital staff to know about? If so, fill in this section.

14   **I would like hospital staff to know the following about the food I eat:**

. . . .

. . . .

15   **I would like hospital staff to know the following information about how and when I normally eat my meals** *(this information may help staff support you if, for example, you normally eat alone and are expected to eat in small groups on the ward):*

. . . .

. . . .

Continued on the next page…

Security and maintenance of your home

If you live alone and would like any of the following tasks undertaken, please tick which ones and add any others you want. Also say who you would like to carry out these tasks.

16 **I would like** . . . . **to secure my property if I haven't done this** (for example: lock doors/windows, turn off the cooker, fires and so on).

I would like . . . . **to dispose of perishable food** (for example: milk, bread, meat, empty the bins and so on).

I would like . . . . **to hold a set of keys to my home in case of an emergency or to collect/return personal items of mine during my stay in hospital.**

Please list any other information or requests that would be useful to you. Show who you would like to have this information:

. . . .

. . . .

. . . .

Please list below the name(s) of people and agencies who you are sharing this information with.

Name . . . .

Address . . . .

Telephone number . . . .

Name . . . .

Address . . . .

Telephone number . . . .

Date of completion of this **Hospital Information Sheet** . . . .

Follow-up date for monitoring effectiveness
of this **Hospital Information Sheet** . . . .

Money and Bills

This section of the pack contains a **Financial Information Sheet** which may be of use to you if:

♦ you are going to be admitted to hospital, *or*

♦ you have been admitted to hospital, *or*

♦ you have had admissions in the past and feel you may again in the future, *or*

♦ you are experiencing difficulties in managing your financial affairs.

When the *Financial Information Sheet* is complete — **KEEP A COPY** for yourself and decide who you most trust to carry out some of the tasks you have identified as being important to you. It can be a friend, a family member, a professional, a service-user group or any other agency that you identify and have an agreement with.

The identified person or persons can have a copy of the *Financial Information Sheet*, or you can give selected information to different people if that is what would work best for you. This information can be updated or changed when necessary.

FINANCIAL INFORMATION SHEET

Personal details

Name . . . .

Address . . . .

. . . . **Telephone no** . . . .

Date of birth . . . . **National Insurance number**. . . . .

Payment by: Giro ☐   Cashbook ☐ **Post Office where cashed** . . . .

. . . .

Amount of benefit paid: £ . . . .

Income support: £ . . . .

Outstanding social fund loans: £ . . . .
  Social fund grants – date applied for . . . . / . . . . . / . . . . ..

Severe disablement allowance: £ . . . .

Invalidity benefit: £ . . . .

Unemployment benefit: £ . . . .

Sickness benefit: £ . . . .

Statutory sick pay: £ . . . .

Retirement pension: £ . . . .

Disability living allowance: £ . . . .

Attendance allowance: £ . . . .
  Do you claim for anyone else? *For example: partner?* Yes ☐ No ☐
  Children? Yes ☐ No ☐ *If **yes**, how many children*. . . . .
  Does anyone else claim for you? Yes ☐ No ☐ *If yes, who?* . . . .

Other savings: £ . . . .

Medical certificates: Sent to DSS? Yes ☐ No ☐   Dated . . . . . / . . . . . / . . . . .

                          Sent by. . . . .

                          DSS office. . . . .

                          Telephone number . . . .

Details of household bills

My order book is . . . .

It is cashed on . . . .

Bills needing payment:	Reference Number *(if applicable)*	Date due	How paid *(for example: meter/key/cash)*
Gas:	. . . .	. . . .	. . . .
Electricity:	. . . .	. . . .	. . . .
Telephone:	. . . .	. . . .	. . . .
Rent:	. . . .	. . . .	. . . .
Council tax:	. . . .	. . . .	. . . .
Water rates:	. . . .	. . . .	. . . .
Other – *(for example: milk/papers/catalogue)*	. . . .	. . . .	

The payment books/bills are in . . . .

Landlord's name . . . .

Landlord's address . . . .

. . . . **Telephone number** . . . .

The following person/people have my agreement to deal with my financial affairs on my behalf:

Name . . . .

Address . . . .

. . . . Telephone number . . . .

Name . . . .

Address . . . .

. . . . Telephone number . . . .

Name . . . .

Address . . . .

. . . . Telephone number . . . .

Signed . . . . **Date** . . . . . / . . . . . / . . . . .

Follow-up date for monitoring effectiveness
of the *Financial Information Sheet*   . . . . . / . . . . . . / . . . . .

Discharge and Aftercare

The aim of this section is to help you prepare for discharge from hospital or psychiatric care and to note what arrangements have been made for aftercare and support. It contains an ***Aftercare Checklist*** to help you do this.

If you are currently on the ward of a psychiatric hospital or unit, then you should start thinking about what your needs will be once you have been discharged. Before you are discharged, ask nursing staff, social workers or advocates to help you complete the ***Aftercare Checklist*** and inform you if you have the right to a care plan.

NB: If you are being discharged after being on Section 3, 37, 47 or 48 of the *Mental Health Act* (1983) it is the law that you must have a care plan. You should demand that the hospital produce a care plan for you.

AFTERCARE CHECKLIST

1 **Your name:**

2 **Your date of birth:**

. . . . / . . . . / . . . .

3 **Your discharge date:**

. . . . / . . . . / . . . .

4 **Discharged from:**

. . . .

. . . .

. . . . Postcode. . . . . Telephone. . . . .

5 **Your new accommodation:**

. . . .

. . . .

. . . . Postcode. . . . . Telephone. . . . .

6 **Your travel arrangements:**

7 **Your social worker:**

Name. . . . .

Team area office. . . . .

. . . . Postcode. . . . . Telephone . . . .

8 **Your CPN:**

Name . . . .

9 **Your social security office:**

. . . .

. . . .

. . . . Postcode. . . . . Telephone . . . .

10 **Your GP:**

. . . .

. . . .

. . . . Postcode. . . . . Telephone . . . .

11 **Your local Job Centre:**

. . . .

. . . .

. . . . Postcode. . . . . Telephone . . . .

12 **Your medication:**

Name of drug   Dosage

13 **Your next outpatient appointment:**

It will be on:

Date . . . . Day . . . .

Time . . . .

Place . . . .

. . . . Postcode . . . . Telephone . . . .

14 **Has a care plan been organised?**   Yes ☐   No ☐

If **yes**, who is your Care Manager?

. . . .

You can contact your Care Manager at:

. . . .

. . . .

. . . .

. . . . Postcode . . . . Telephone . . . .

15 **Have you had a benefits check?**   Yes ☐   No ☐

What are you claiming for?

. . . .

. . . .

. . . .

16 **What arrangements have been made for day-care, sheltered work, or other activities?**

. . . .

. . . .

. . . .

. . . .

17 **What support networks will you have in the community?** *For example: family, friends, advocates?*

. . . .

. . . .

. . . .

. . . .

Notes for Mental Health Workers About the Use of the Direct Power Resource Pack

by Thurstine Basset

This section contains notes for mental health workers who have acquired the Direct Power Resource Pack and want to include it in their work with service users.

This section covers the following areas:

1. Who are the mental health workers who might use **Direct Power**?

2. Brief description of **Direct Power**:
   - ◆ what **Direct Power** is
   - ◆ how it was developed and used
   - ◆ the aims of **Direct Power**.

3. Notes on the use of the **Direct Power** pack:
   - ◆ current climate — legislation and guidelines
   - ◆ empowering service users
   - ◆ involving carers / relatives.
   - ◆ enabling service users to use **Direct Power**.

4. Notes on use for each individual section of the pack.

1. Who are the mental health workers who might use Direct Power?

Direct Power is written for people who use mental health services. As a mental health worker, your task is to enable service users to use **Direct Power**.

You may be an:

♦ advocate/advocacy worker

♦ community care worker

♦ day-care worker

♦ GP

♦ housing worker/residential-project worker

♦ mental health nurse

♦ occupational therapist

♦ physiotherapist

♦ psychiatrist

♦ psychologist

♦ service-user group or carer group worker/co-ordinator

♦ social worker

♦ voluntary worker.

2. Brief description of Direct Power

♦ what **Direct Power** is

♦ how the pack was developed

♦ the aims of **Direct Power**.

What Direct Power is

Direct Power is a resource pack for people who want to develop their own care plans and support networks.

Notes for Mental Health Workers

Direct Power has eight sections:

◆ **Section One: Direct Power** and Community Care

◆ **Section Two:** Building Your Own Personal Profile
(Including: *Your Personal Profile* and *Current Circumstances: Checklist*)

◆ **Section Three:** Experience of Services You Are in Contact With

◆ **Section Four:** *Self-assessment of Needs: Checklist*

◆ **Section Five:** *Priority Action List*

◆ **Section Six:** Further Help
(Including: *Help and Support Directory* and *Agency Contact Sheet*)

◆ **Section Seven:** Partnership Agreements

◆ **Section Eight:** Hospital and Home
(Including: *Hospital Information Sheet*, *Financial Information Sheet*
and *Aftercare Checklist*).

How the pack was developed

Direct Power was originally developed by the Community Support Network and Brixton Community Sanctuary in London. Both organisations are service-user-led. They developed **Direct Power** so that service users could gain more control over their care plans and support networks. The pack has been used extensively since August 1993 and has been adapted as a result of this use for this publication.

The aims of Direct Power

Direct Power has a number of aims addressed directly to service users:

◆ to guide you through the maze of community care

◆ to let you develop and construct a personal profile about yourself

◆ for you to comment on any service you are or have been in contact with

◆ to help you to undertake a self-assessment of your needs and then to identify and make contact with agencies that may be able to provide you with appropriate support, advice and information

◆ to provide you with information and advice that will enable you to develop and construct your own support network and care plan

◆ to help you to identify what you and any agency need to have agreements on and how to help you develop a partnership agreement

◆ to help you decide on your support needs if you are either admitted to or discharged from hospital.

3. Notes on the use of the Direct Power pack

Current climate – Legislation and guidelines

As a mental health worker, you will be involved in working with service users in assessing their needs and agreeing care plans, which will be reviewed and monitored.

Following the introduction of the *Mental Health Act* in 1983 and Community Care legislation in the 1990s, the spotlight has fallen on mental health services as we approach the new millennium.

The closure of large psychiatric hospitals and the provision of comprehensive Community Care services is absolutely central to current health and social care policy and provision.

Legislation and guidelines have been produced in the 1990s to assist mental health workers in providing Community Care services.

Empowering service users

Legislation, guidelines and many key reports and publications are all agreed that people who use mental health services must be central to those services, which must reflect their needs. Past models of service provision have been shown to be disempowering. Current models must ensure that service users have sufficient power to influence the services and how they are provided.

Direct Power will help mental health workers in their quest to empower service users.

Involving carers/relatives

As a mental health worker, it is also crucially important that you engage with carers/ relatives. They are often the main source of support for service users within 'care in the community'.

You should not assume that service users and carers/relatives have the same needs, but neither should you assume that their needs are dramatically different. Relationships between service users and carers/relatives may vary greatly. In some situations there will be co-operation and agreement; in others, there may be adversity and disagreement. Carers/relatives are often under a great deal of stress themselves and may be entitled to an assessment of their own needs under Community Care legislation.

Direct Power enables service users to explore their own care and support networks and this includes any care and support that they may be receiving from a carer/relative.

Enabling service users to use **Direct Power**

If you are working with a particular service user, you will need to discuss and decide with them whether they should gradually work through all eight sections of the pack over time, completing each part before moving on to the next, or whether they should take the pack and complete it all at the same time/sitting. Some service users will want the whole pack from the start, others may prefer to take a section at a time and build up their resources gradually.

Service users will also have different preferences about how they work through **Direct Power**. Some may prefer to work through it on their own, others with a friend or advocate. Some may want to complete it in a group of service users, others with a carer/relative or a mental health worker. It may be that a combination of all these approaches may suit some.

Your role as a mental health worker, possibly as the keyworker, is to enable the service user to complete **Direct Power** in the way that they feel suits them best.

4. Notes on use for each individual section of the pack

Section One: **Direct Power** and Community Care

This section explains what Community Care is and shows how **Direct Power** will help service users through the maze of assessment and access to services. It does not require any writing. If service users have any questions about Community Care, you should be ready to answer them. It will help if you are aware of how Care Management and the Care Programme Approach combine in your area.

Section Two: Building Your Own Personal Profile

It is important in this section that the service user is able to map out his or her own personal profile and current situation. If service users ask for support or help with this, it is important to stress that this is a strengths-based holistic personal profile and that it is not just about the person as a user of mental health services.

Section Three: Experience of Services You Are in Contact With

If service users need any assistance in completing this section, it should be given by somebody not connected with the services being used or described, possibly an advocate or a friend.

Section Four: Self-assessment of Needs: Checklist

This section is quite easy to complete. It involves ticking boxes, indicating where service users feel they need help and support.

Section Five: Priority Action List

Following on from Section Four, the Priority Action List gives service users the opportunity to put their needs in order of priority. It may be helpful for service users to write each separate need on a card or small piece of paper and sift them around before placing them in order of priority and then completing this section.

Section Six: Further Help

This section aims to help service users to identify agencies that can be helpful in relation to the areas that they have identified as their priority needs. There is a key role here for yourself as a local worker, since the list in **Direct Power** is mainly of London-based agencies and organisations. You can greatly assist service users in completing this section by making them aware of local services. There is probably a directory of services in your area.

Section Seven: Partnership Agreements

Encourage the service user to complete these agreements with organisations that are able to offer a service to meet his or her needs. You may be able to be of assistance here, particularly if you are not a part of the service being offered.

Section Eight: Hospital and Home

This section helps service users think through what support they might need if they are either admitted to or discharged from hospital. This is very important information and service users are encouraged to give a copy of it to a person whom they can trust to carry out the various tasks. If that person is you, then you can ensure that this happens. If the person is someone else, you need to be in touch with the chosen person at times of admission or discharge.

Three Final Points

◆ Make sure you read **Direct Power** and are familiar with it before discussing it with service users.

◆ Never forget that **Direct Power** is essentially the property of the service user who completes it.

◆ Any assistance that you give to service users in completing **Direct Power** must be enabling and empowering to the service user.